MAX'S SCOOTER

Written by Meredith Costain
Illustrated by Kate Curtis

Max is learning to ride his new scooter.

He pushes off with his foot to make it move.

Max pushes his foot down faster and faster.

The scooter moves faster too.

See how Max is holding the handlebars straight?

His scooter travels in a straight line as well.

Oh no! A prickly rose bush is in the way.

Max will have to turn left or he will crash into it.

Yes! He's pushed the handlebar with his right hand and pulled it with his left hand.

His scooter has turned just in time.

Oh no! Now Bear is in the way.

Max will have to turn right this time.

He's pushed the handlebar with his left hand
and pulled it with his right hand.

Phew! That was close!

Max has had enough of scooters for today.

He drags his foot along the ground until the scooter stops.

Parent and Teacher Notes

The story of Max's Scooter looks at the science of forces:

Forces are pushes and pulls that make things move. Something will only start or stop moving because we have pushed or pulled it. The harder we push or pull, the faster the object will move.

EXPERIMENT
Make Your Own Obstacle Course

What you need:
- a large, safe open area in a park or playground
- a set of obstacles e.g. witches' hats, rubbish bins, soft or plastic toys
- a scooter or tricycle for each child.

What you do:

1. Set up a simple obstacle course for a group of children to race around, one by one.

2. Create a starting and finishing line, then place the obstacles around the course so that the children will need to make a series of right and left turns to avoid crashing into them.

3. The child who manages to successfully negotiate the course in the shortest time is the winner.

More …

Have you ever watched a caterpillar move? It uses force to move itself along. As it moves, it pushes out the front half of its body, then pulls in the back half.

How Does a Scooter Move?

1. Pushing against the ground with your foot will make the scooter move.

2. It will keep moving at the same speed in a straight line until a force changes its speed or direction.

3. If you want the scooter to turn a corner, you need to make forces act on it. To make the handlebar turn you pull back with one hand and push forward with the other hand.

4. Friction is a force that slows things down. It is caused when two objects rub together. Dragging your foot along the ground creates a lot of friction. This will slow the scooter until it eventually stops.

About the Author

Meredith Costain is a versatile, award-winning author who specialises in books for early childhood. Many of her titles have sold internationally or been adapted for television, audio or multi-media. She lives in inner-city Melbourne with a menagerie of pets, who frequently feature in her stories.

About the Illustrator

Kate Curtis has had fun drawing pictures in advertising, animation and comics for a very long time, and counts dogs among her closest friends. She divides her time between a very old house in inner-city Melbourne and a very old house at Point Lonsdale.

The Five Mile Press Pty Ltd
1 Centre Road, Scoresby
Victoria 3179 Australia
www.fivemile.com.au

Written by Meredith Costain

Science at Play series copyright © The Five Mile Press, 2009
Text copyright © The Five Mile Press, 2009
Illustrations copyright © Kate Curtis, 2009
All rights reserved
Series editor: Niki Horin

First published 2009

Printed in China 5 4 3 2 1

National Library of Australia Cataloguing-in-Publication data
 Costain, Meredith, 1955-
 Max's scooter / Meredith Costain ; illustrator, Kate Curtis.
 9781742115009 (hbk.)
 Costain, Meredith, 1955- Science at play ; 2.
 For primary school age.
 Forse and energy--Juvenile literature
 Other Authors/Contributors: Curtis, Kate.
531.6